This book belongs to : Jennifer Thomas

audition
songs for kids

C000149026

£13-50

Wise Publications
London/New York/Paris/Sydney/Copenhagen/Madrid/Tokyo

Exclusive Distributors:
Music Sales Limited
8/9 Frith Street,
London W1V 5TZ, England.

Music Sales Pty Limited
120 Rothschild Avenue,
Rosebery, NSW 2018, Australia.

Order No. AM955273
ISBN 0-7119-7883-2
This book © Copyright 1999 by Wise Publications

Book design by Miranda Harvey
Compiled by Peter Evans
Music arranged by Paul Honey
Music processed by Enigma Music Production Services

CD performed and recorded by Paul Honey

Printed in the United Kingdom by
Printwise Limited, Haverhill, Suffolk.

Your Guarantee of Quality
As publishers, we strive to produce every book to the highest commercial standards.
The music has been freshly engraved and the book has been carefully designed to
minimise awkward page turns and to make playing from it a real pleasure.
Particular care has been given to specifying acid-free, neutral-sized paper made from
pulps which have not been elemental chlorine bleached. This pulp is from farmed
sustainable forests and was produced with special regard for the environment.
Throughout, the printing and binding have been planned to ensure a sturdy,
attractive publication which should give years of enjoyment.
If your copy fails to meet our high standards, please inform us and we will
gladly replace it.

Music Sales' complete catalogue describes thousands of titles and is available in full
colour sections by subject, direct from Music Sales Limited. Please state your areas of
interest and send a cheque/postal order for £1.50 for postage to:
Music Sales Limited, Newmarket Road, Bury St. Edmunds, Suffolk IP33 3YB.

www.musicsales.com

Any Dream Will Do

Music by Andrew Lloyd Webber
Lyrics by Tim Rice

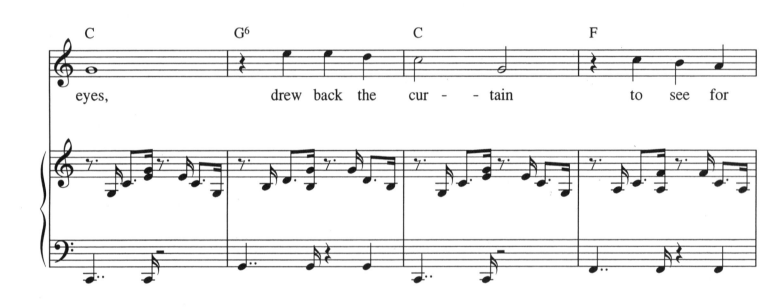

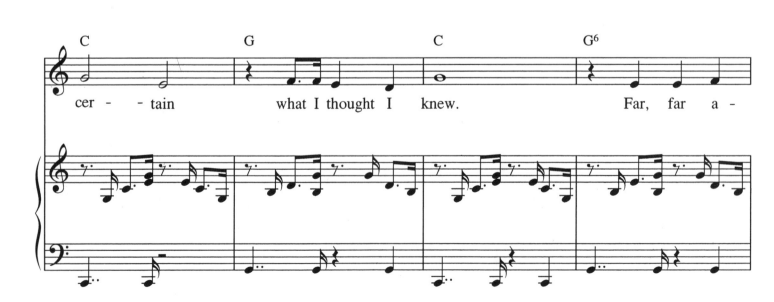

Consider Yourself

Words & Music by Lionel Bart

Bright march tempo

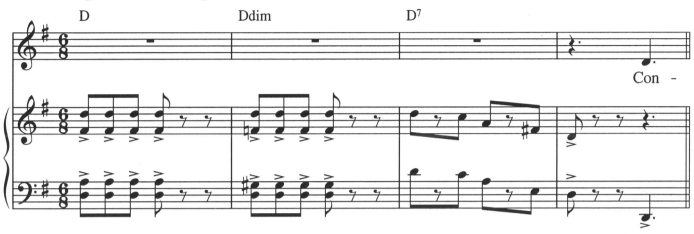

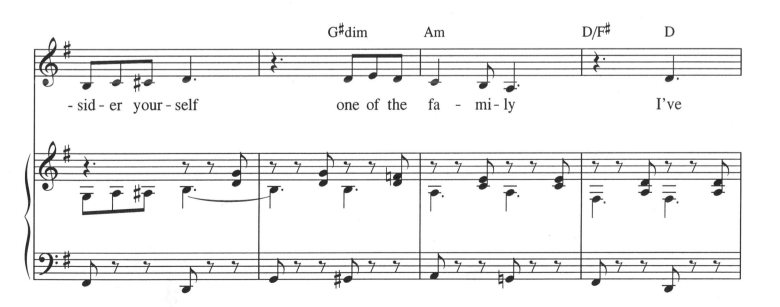

ta-ken to you so strong, It's

clear we're go-ing to get a - long! Con -

- sid - er your - self well in: Con -

- sid-er your-self part of the fur - ni - ture. There

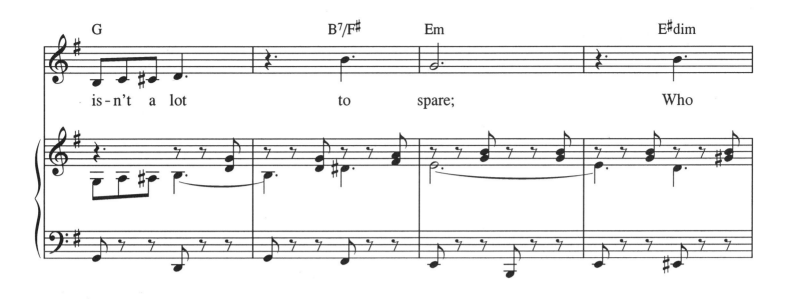

is-n't a lot to spare; Who

cares? What - - ev-er we've got we share!

If it should
No-bo-dy

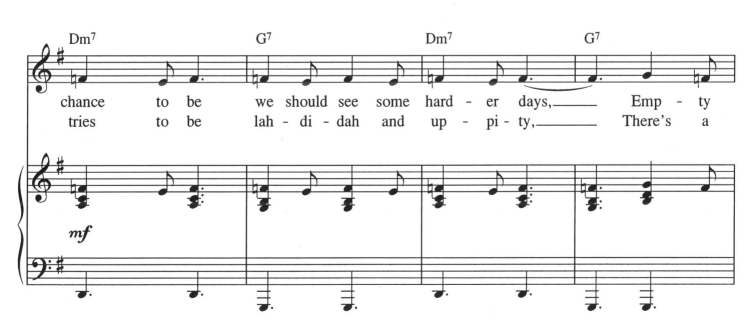

chance to be we should see some hard-er days,_____ Emp - ty
tries to be lah - di - dah and up - pi - ty,_____ There's a

I'd Do Anything

Words & Music by Lionel Bart

Moderately

I'd do an-y-thing for you, dear, an-y-thing, For

you mean ev-'ry-thing to me. I know that

Verse 2:
(Would you lace my shoe?) Anything!
(Paint your face bright blue?) Anything!
(Catch a kangaroo?) Anything!
(Go to Timbuctoo?) And back again!
I'd risk everything, *etc.*

Verse 3:
Let the clouds of grey come along,
Never mind if they come along.
Surely they won't stay very long,
If you'll only say you're mine alone.
I'd risk everything, *etc.*

No Matter What

Music by Andrew Lloyd Webber
Lyrics by Jim Steinman

Moderately

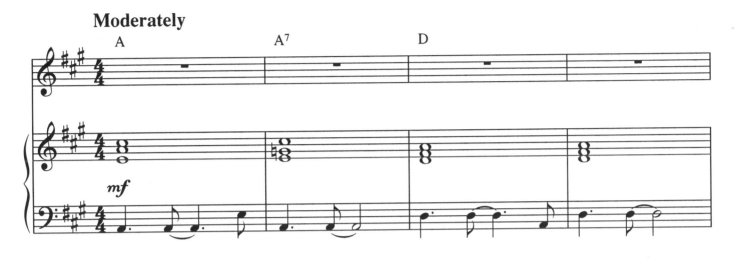

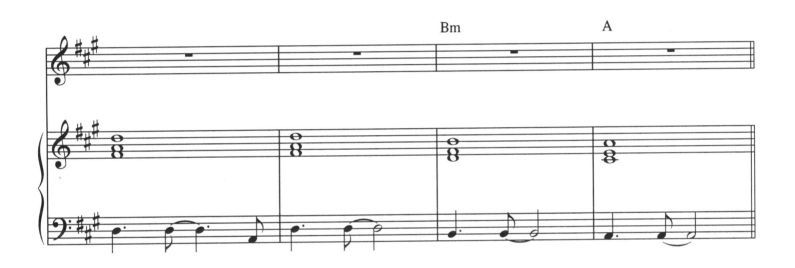

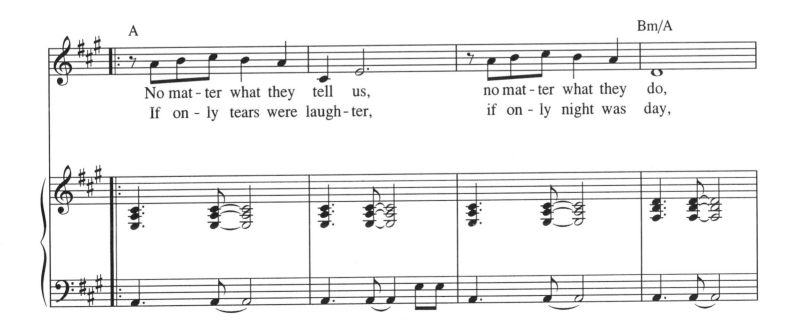

No mat - ter what they tell us,   no mat - ter what they do,
If on - ly tears were laugh - ter,   if on - ly night was day,

Spice Up Your Life

Words & Music by Geri Halliwell, Emma Bunton, Melanie Brown,
Melanie Chisholm, Victoria Aadams, Richard Stannard & Matt Rowe

Moderate Samba feel

La la la la la la la la la la

la la la la la la la. La la la la la la

Verse 2:

Yellow men in Timbuktu

Colour for both me and you.

Kungfu fighting, dancing queen,

Tribal spaceman and all that's in between.

Colours of the world, *etc.*

Thank You For The Music

Words & Music by Benny Andersson & Björn Ulvaeus

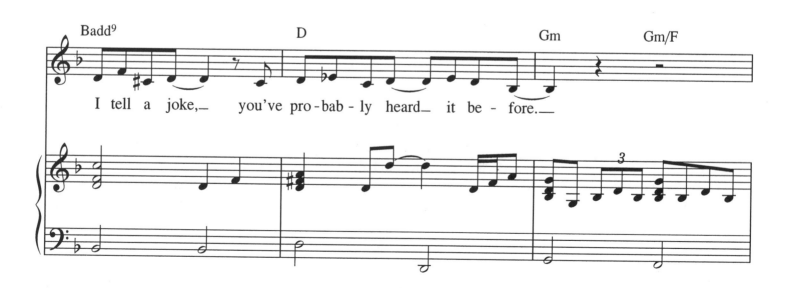

But I have a ta-lent, a won-der-ful thing,— 'cause

ev-ery-one lis-tens when I start to sing.— I'm so grate-ful and proud,—

all I want— is to sing— it out loud— So I say

thank you for the mu-sic, the songs I'm sing-ing, thanks for all the

Well who-ev - er it was— I'm a fan,— So I say

CODA

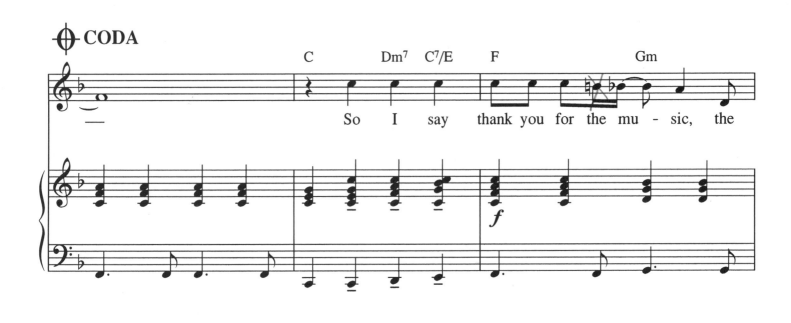

So I say thank you for the mu - sic, the

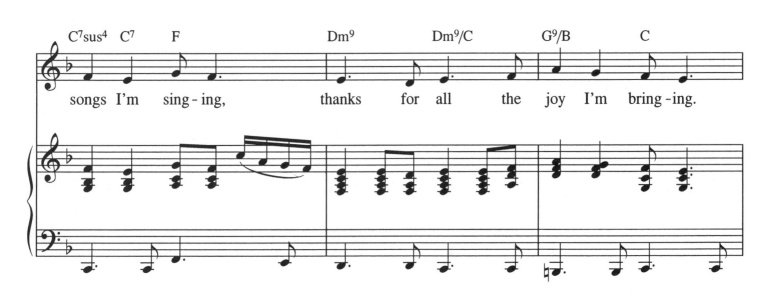

songs I'm sing-ing, thanks for all the joy I'm bring-ing.

The Candy Man

Words & Music by Leslie Bricusse & Anthony Newley

Who can take a sun - rise,___ sprin - kle it with dew,_____
(Verse 2, see block lyric)

cov - er it in choc -'late and a mi - ra - cle or two? The can - dy man,___

the can - dy man can.___ The can - dy man can 'cause he

Verse 2:
Who can take a rainbow
Wrap it in a sigh,
Soak it in the sun and make a strawberry lemon pie?
The candy man, the candy man can.
The candy man can 'cause he mixes it with love
And makes the world taste good.

Tomorrow

Words by Martin Charnin
Music by Charles Strouse

Moderately

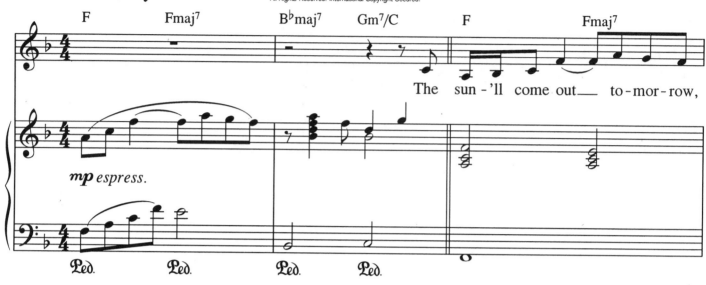

The sun -'ll come out___ to-mor-row,

bet your bot-tom dol-lar that to-mor-row___ there'll be sun! Jus'

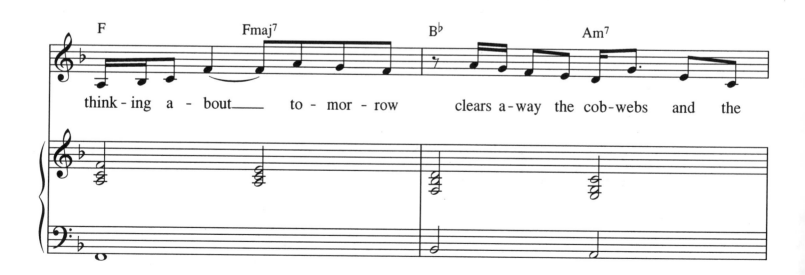

think-ing a-bout___ to-mor-row clears a-way the cob-webs and the

love ya, to-mor-row, you're al-ways a day a-way.

Oh, the sun-'ll come out___ to-mor-row, Oh I got to hang on 'til to-

-mor-row___ come what may. To-mor-row, to-mor-row, I

When I'm Sixty Four

Words & Music by John Lennon & Paul McCartney

birth-day greet-ings, bot-tle of wine?— If I'd been out till quar-ter to three—

would you lock the door?— Will you still need— me, will you still feed— me

when I'm six-ty four?

You'll be old - er too.—————

And if you say the word__ I could

stay with you.

I could be han - dy mend-ing a fuse__ when your lights have gone.__
(Verse 2 see block lyric)

You can knit a sweat-er by the fire__ side,__ Sun-day morn-ings, go for a ride.__

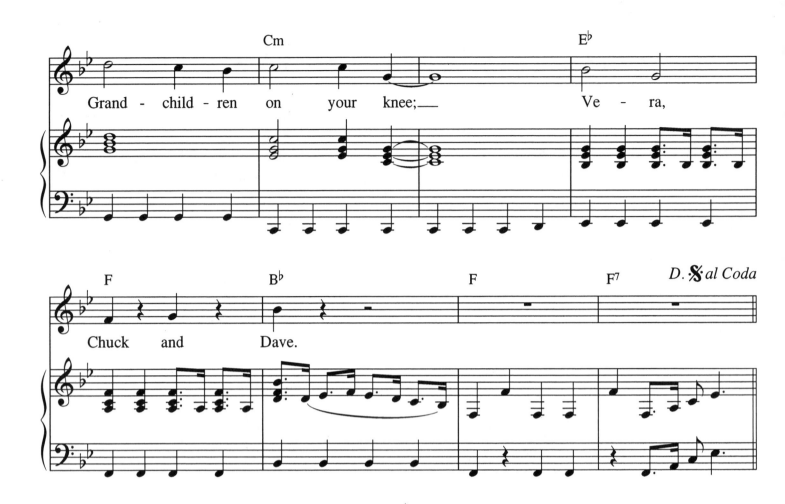

Grand - child - ren on your knee;___ Ve - ra,

Chuck and Dave.

D. 𝄊 al Coda

CODA

four?

Verse 2:
Send me a postcard, drop me a line
Stating point of view.
Indicate precisely what you mean to say
Yours sincerely wasting away.
Give me your answer, fill in a form,
Mine for ever more.
Will you still need me, will you still feed me,
When I'm sixty four?

Other great book and CD titles...

Audition Songs for Female Singers 1
Don't Cry For Me Argentina...
plus Adelaide's Lament; Big Spender; Heaven Help My Heart; I Cain't Say No;
I Will Survive; Out Here On My Own; Saving All My Love For You;
Someone To Watch Over Me; The Wind Beneath My Wings.
Order No. AM92587

Audition Songs for Female Singers 2
I Dreamed A Dream...
plus Another Suitcase In Another Hall; Fame; If I Were A Bell; Miss Byrd;
Save The Best For Last; Someone Else's Story; There Are Worse Things I Could Do;
What I Did For Love; You Can Always Count On Me.
Order No. AM950224

Audition Songs for Female Singers 3
Memory...
plus Can't Help Lovin' Dat Man; Crazy; Diamonds Are A Girl's Best Friend;
Now That I've Seen Her; Show Me Heaven; That Ole Devil Called Love;
The Reason; The Winner Takes It All; Wishing You Were Somehow Here Again.
Order No. AM955284

Audition Songs for Female Singers 4
I Don't Know How To Love Him...
plus As Long As He Needs Me; Constant Craving; Feeling Good;
I Say A Little Prayer; If My Friends Could See Me Now; It's Oh So Quiet;
Killing Me Softly With His Song; Tell Me It's Not True; You Must Love Me.
Order No. AM955295

Audition Songs for Male Singers 1
Tonight...
plus All Good Gifts; Anthem; Being Alive; Corner Of The Sky; Funny;
High Flying, Adored; If I Loved You; Luck Be A Lady; Why, God, Why?.
Order No. AM92586

Audition Songs for Male Singers 2
Maria...
plus All I Need Is The Girl; Bring Him Home; Frederick's Aria;
I Don't Remember Christmas; Sit Down, You're Rocking The Boat;
Some Enchanted Evening; This Is The Moment; Where I Want To Be;
You're Nothing Without Me.
Order No. AM950213

CD Track Listing

1 Any Dream Will Do
(Lloyd Webber/Rice) The Really Useful Group Ltd.

2 Consider Yourself
(Bart) Lakeview Music Publishing Company Ltd.

3 I'd Do Anything
(Bart) Lakeview Music Publishing Company Ltd.

4 No Matter What
(Lloyd Webber/Steinman) The Really Useful Group Ltd. &
Lost Boys Music/PolyGram Music Publishing Ltd.

5 Spice Up Your Life
(Halliwell/Bunton/Brown/Chisholm/Aadams/Stannard/Rowe)
Windswept Pacific Music Ltd./PolyGram Music Publishing Ltd.

6 Thank You For The Music
(Andersson/Ulvaeus) Bocu Music Ltd.

7 The Candy man
(Bricusse/Newley) BMG Music Publishing Ltd.

8 Tomorrow
(Charnin/Strouse) Chappell-Morris Music Ltd./
Peermusic (UK) Ltd.

9 When I'm Sixty Four
(Lennon/McCartney) Northern Songs/Sony/ATV Music
Publishing (UK) Ltd.

MCPS